THEATRE ROYAL—DRURY LANE

The Theatre Royal Drury Lane Production of

SHOW BOAT

A MUSICAL PLAY

Adapted from Edna Ferber's novel of the same name

MUSIC BY

JEROME KERN

BOOK AND LYRICS BY

OSCAR HAMMERSTEIN 2nd

CHAPPELL & CO. LTD. 50, NEW BOND STREET, LONDON, W. 1 and SYDNEY	**T. B. HARMS COMPANY** 62-64, WEST 45TH STREET NEW YORK

SHOW BOAT

CAST OF CHARACTERS

(In the order of their appearance)

WINDY	JACK MARTIN
STEVE	COLIN CLIVE
PETE	FRED HEARNE
QUEENIE	ALBERTA HUNTER
PARTHY ANN HAWKS	VIOLA COMPTON
CAPTAIN ANDY	CEDRIC HARDWICKE
ELLIE	DOROTHY LENA
FRANK	LESLIE SARONY
RUBBER FACE	HENRY THOMAS
JULIE	MARIE BURKE
GAYLORD RAVENAL	HOWETT WORSTER
VALLON	PERCY PARSONS
MAGNOLIA	EDITH DAY
JOE	PAUL ROBESON
FARO DEALER	WILLIAM WALLACE
GAMBLER	ALEC J. WILLARD
LOUNGER	FELIX HILL
BACKWOODSMAN	ROY EMERTON
JEB	GORDON CROCKER
LA BELLE FATIMA	LENORE GADSDEN
OLD SPORT	CECIL DEREHAM
LANDLADY	MARGARET YARDE
ETHEL	KATHLEEN THOMAS
KIM (as Young Woman)	EDITH DAY
JAKE (Piano Player)	MICHAEL COLE
MAX	WILL STUART
MAN (with Guitar)	WALTER WEBSTER
CHARLIE (Doorman at Trocadero)	NORRIS SMITH
LOTTIE	NANCY BROWN
DOLLY	PEGGY LOVAT
HAZEL	ANN BARBOUR

Mississippi Chorus led and directed by John Payne

SYNOPSIS OF SCENES

ACT I

Scene 1. The Levee at Natchez on the Mississippi—*in the late Eighteen-eighties*.

Scene 2. Kitchen Pantry of the " Cotton Blossom "—*a Half Hour Later*.

Scene 3. Outside a Waterfront Gambling Saloon—*Simultaneous with Scene 2*.

Scene 4. Auditorium and Stage of the " Cotton Blossom "—*One Hour Later*.

Scene 5. Box-office, on Foredeck of the " Cotton Blossom "—*Three Weeks Later*.

Scene 6. Auditorium and Stage of the " Cotton Blossom "—During the Third Act of " The Parson's Bride "—*That Evening*.

Scene 7. The Top Deck of the " Cotton Blossom " —*Later that Night*.

Scene 8. The Levee—*Next Morning*.

ACT II

Scene 1. A Midway Plaisance, Chicago World's Fair, 1893.

Scene 2. A Room on Ontario Street, 1904.

Scene 3. Rehearsal Room of the Trocadero Music Hall—*About 5 p.m.*

Scene 4. Trocadero Music Hall—*New Year's Eve*, 11.30, 1904.

Scene 5. In front of the Office of " The Natchez Evening Democrat," 1927.

Scene 6. Top Deck of the new " Cotton Blossom," 1927.

Scene 7. Levee at Natchez—*the Next Night*.

Scenery Designed and Painted by JOSEPH AND PHIL HARKER.

Dances and Ensembles by MAX SCHECK.

Orchestra under the Direction of HERMAN FINCK.

The Play Produced by FELIX EDWARDES

SHOW BOAT

OVERTURE

Lyrics by
OSCAR HAMMERSTEIN IInd

Music by
JEROME KERN

Copyright, MCMXXVIII, by T. B. HARMS. C?
Chappell & C?, Ltd., 50, New Bond Street, London, W.1 & Sydney.

6

② Ben sostenuto

③ Brass

Chappell

Chappell

Chappell

Andante moderato

Chappell

No. 1

Opening Act I
The Levee At Natchez On The Mississippi

Lyrics by
OSCAR HAMMERSTEIN IInd

Music by
JEROME KERN

white men play Load - in' up boats wid de

bales of cot - ton, Git-tin' no rest till de judg - ment day.

Women
Coloured
Chorus

Git yo'self a bran'new gal, A lov-in' ba-by who's de ap-ple of yo' eye.

Men

Hey! Git a - long, git a - long, Git a - long, git a-long.

Chappell

Chappell

Chappell

16

Chappell

Chappell

Chappell

20

Capriccioso

Enter a group of mincing misses.

Chappell

Chappell

Girls: lot we know!

Boys: These are not the days of old.

Boys: See!——— The show boat! That's old Cap-tain An-dy's "Cot-ton Blos-som," will you

Boys: go?——— let me take you to the show?———

Coloured Women: H'yah! look

Chappell

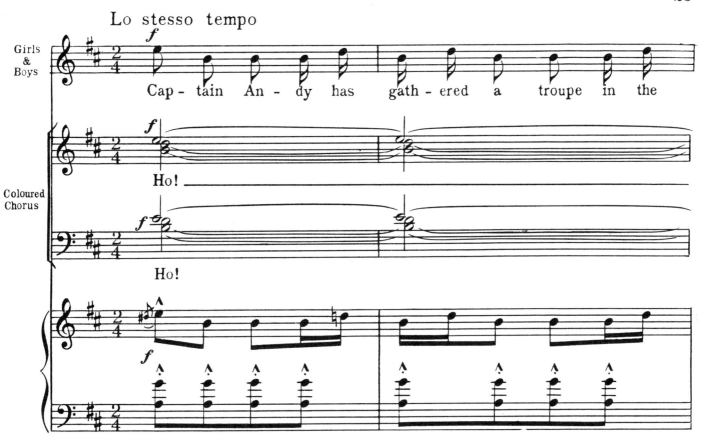

Chappell

Girls & Boys: hand-som-est lead-ing man And beau-ti-ful Ju-lie La-verne as

Coloured Chorus: Ho!

Girls & Boys: well. "Cot-ton Blos-som," Cap-tain An-dy's float-ing show!

Coloured Chorus: Cot-ton blos-som, cot-ton blos-som, Love to see you grow-in' free,

Chappell

Chappell

Chappell

Parthy Ann appears. "Andy Hawks! Drat that man, He's never around!"

Adagio pesante *(falteringly)*

Piano off stage

(Dialogue)

The band appears, led by Captain Andy with a couple of town girls on each arm.

(Orchestra)

Chappell

Allegretto

GIRLS

Cap-tain An-dy, Cap-tain An-dy, here's your le-mon cake and home made can-dy.

Quince pre-serve and ap-ple brand-y; Ma-ma sends her best re-gards to you.

GIRLS & BOYS

Cap-tain An-dy, Cap-tain An-dy, we've been hear-ing all a-bout your dan-dy

show. Is this year's good as last year? Won't you tell us what is new?

Chappell

Captain Andy's Bally-Hoo

Chappell

CAPTAIN ANDY (*Spoken*)

Look it we got! Look it we got! How can we fail? How can we fail? You nev-er seen a show like this be - fore!

(*Sung*)

We'll try to make the even-ing bright An' if you come a -round to-night, To - mor-row night you'll come a -round for more.—

Lo stesso tempo
GIRLS & BOYS

Cap-tain An - dy, Cap - tain An - dy, you know how to make a

Chappell

33

34

Dancette..ELLIE & FRANK.

STEVE:"*I reckon, I won't do any more talkin' about it.*"

lunga

8va

f marc.

29678

Chappell

Pete and Steve struggle.

Allegro

ENSEMBLE exit.

"Cot-ton Blos-som," "Cot-ton Blos-som," Cap-tain An-dy's float-ing show.

Thrills and laugh-ter, con-cert af-ter, get your girl and go!

Chappell

Giocoso

PARTHY :*"I'll have more to say to you later!"* (Parthy exit)

Andy, seeing that Parthy is quite gone, answers her boldly.

lunga

Lento (*melos*)

Parthy off stage: "Andy!"

Meno

CAPTAIN ANDY:*"Just one big happy family Bah!"* (exit)

Dolce e moderato

For the first time Ravenal is seen looking moodily at the river.

Chappell

Ellie is attracted by Ravenal's appearance --

- - - - - - - She drops her handkerchief.

rall. molto

Broad

Enter Vallon.

(Dialogue)

Horn

Andante moderato

Chappell

C Andante moderato

mp RAVENAL

Who cares if my boat goes up stream,— or if the

gale bids me go with the riv-er's flow?——

I drift a - long with my fan - cy, —— Some - times I thank my luck - y stars my heart is free, —————— And oth - er times I won - der where's the mate for me? ——————

Piano off stage. Ravenal listens, amused at the poor rendition.

falteringly

mf

Chappell

The drift wood float-ing o-ver the sea Some day finds a shel-ter-ing lee,

So some-where there sure-ly must be A har-bour meant for me.

Chappell

Magnolia appears on upper deck of "Cotton Blossom" and sees Ravenal.

(He sees Magnolia and stops short)

I drift a - long with my fan - cy,——— Some - times I thank my luck - y stars my heart is free,——— And oth - er times I won - der where's the mate?

MAGNOLIA
Hel - lo!

RAVENAL
Er - How'd you do?

Chappell

Moderato *molto espressivo through dialogue.*

Make-Believe

(Ravenal and Magnolia)

Chappell

Chappell

(Magnolia draws back)

tell the truth,——— I do.——— Your par-don I

pray,——— 'Twas too much to say——— the words that be-

tray my heart.——— We on-ly pre-

MAGNOLIA

tend,——— You do not of-fend——— In play-ing a

Chappell

lov - er's part.———

Allegretto

p MAGNOLIA

The game of— just sup-pos-ing— is the sweet-est— game I know;—

Our— dreams are more— ro - man-tic than the world we see.

RAVENAL

And if the things we dream a - bout don't hap-pen to be so,—

That's just an un-im-port-ant tech-ni-cal-i-ty.

Poco animato

MAGNOLIA

Tho' the cold and brut-al fact is You and I have nev-er met.

We need not mind con-ven-tion's P's and Q's,——— If we put our thoughts in

Ob.

(con Ped.)

Chappell

prac - tice, We can ban-ish all re - gret Im-ag-in-

ing most an - y - thing we choose.———— We could

make be-lieve———— I love you,———— We could make be-lieve———

That you love me.———— Oth - ers find peace of

Chappell

Chappell

Ol' Man River

(Joe and Male Chorus)

Dere's an ol' man called de Mis - sis - sip - pi,

Dat's de ol' man dat I'd like to be; What does he care if de

world's got trou-bles? What does he care if de land ain't free?

Ol' man Riv - er, dat ol' man Riv - er, He mus' know sump - in', But

Chappell

Chappell

You an' me we sweat an' strain,

Bod-y all ach-in' an' racked wid pain. "Tote dat barge!"

"Lift dat bale!" Git a lit-tle drunk an' you'll

land in jail. Ah gits wear-y an' sick of try-in', Ah'm

Chappell

tired of liv-in' an' scared of dy-in', But ol' man Riv-er, He

jes' keeps rol-lin' a - lon'

Horns

Moderato

Col - oured folks work on de Mis - sis - sip - pi,

(Stevedores appear carrying various loads and group around Joe)

(Curtains close in on group)

Col-oured folks work while de white folks play Pul-lin' dose boats, from de

Chappell

down to sun-set Git-tin' no rest till de judg-ment day.

Mosso

COLOURED MALE CHORUS

Don't look up, an' don't look down, You don't dast make de

Violins

white boss frown. Bend your knees an'

bow yo' head, An' pull dat rope un-til you're dead.

Chappell

Chappell

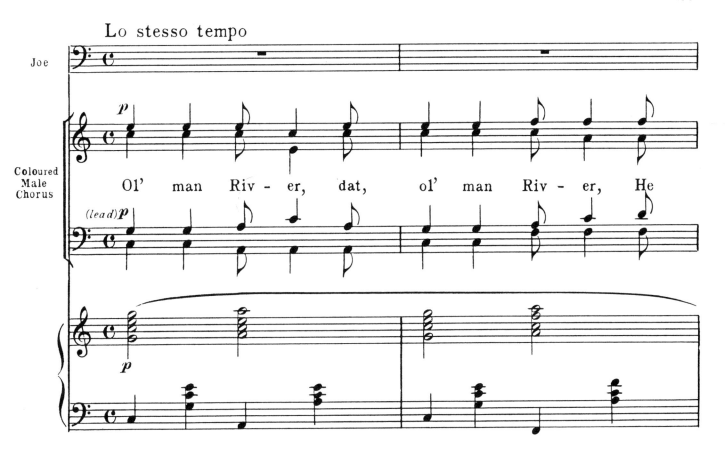

Chappell

Chappell

Joe

Coloured
Male
Chorus

don't plant cot-ton an' dem dat plants 'em is soon for-got-ten; But

(lead)

Joe

Lon' ol' riv-er keeps

Coloured
Male
Chorus

Ol' man Riv-er, He jes' keeps rol-lin' a lon'

pp

Chappell

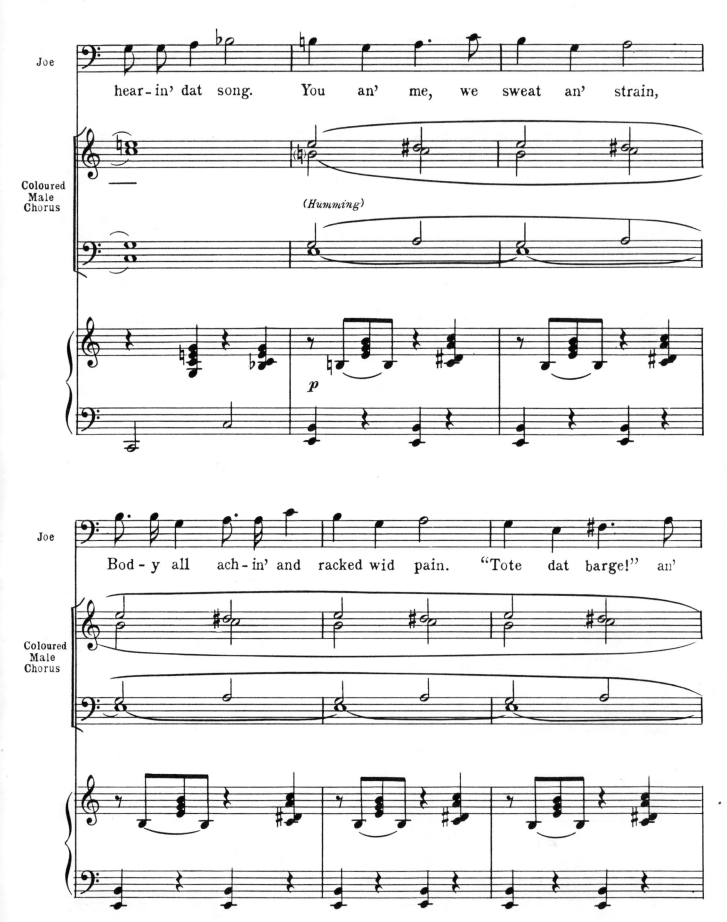

Chappell

Joe

Lift dat bale!" We gits a lit - tle drunk an' we

Coloured Male Chorus

Joe

lands in jail. Ah gits wear-y an' sick of try-in', Ah'm

Coloured Male Chorus

Ah gits wear-y an' sick of try-in', Ah'm

Chappell

Chappell

Scene II

Kitchen Pantry of the "Cotton Blossom"

Piano

Curtain *Magnolia is discovered seated at the table.*

Chappell

Can't Help Lovin' Dat Man

(Julie, Queenie, Magnolia, Joe and Mixed Quartet)

Chappell

can't help lov-in' dat man— of mine. *(Through dialogue)*

Solo Violin

pp

p JULIE

Oh, lis-ten, sis-ter, I love my Mis-ter man—— and I can't—

p

Chappell

tell yo' why,— Dere ain't no rea-son why I should love dat

man.——— It must be sump-in' dat—

— De an - gels done plan.———

Fish got to swim— and birds got to fly,— I got to love— one

Chappell

Chappell

cresc. e piu appass.

When he goes a - way——

cresc. e piu appass.

Dat's a rain-y day,——— And when he comes

back dat day is fine,— The sun .will shine.

He can come home— as late as can be,— Home with-out him— ain't

Chappell

no home to me,— Can't help lov-in' dat man— of mine.

Poco meno
Enter Joe

pp QUEENIE

Mah man is shift-less An' good fo' noth-in'

molto rall. *a tempo.*

too,— He's mah man— jes' de same.— He's nev-er near me

when dere is work to do. —————

Queenie: He's nev-er roun' me when — dere's work-in' to do. —

Joe: He's nev-er roun yo' when — dere's work-in' to do. —

Queenie: De chim-ley's smok-in', De roof is leak-in'

Chappell

74

29678 Chappell

Chappell

Chappell

Chappell

Chappell

Chappell

Chappell

Chappell

(For encore see top of page 75.)

Chappell

Scene III
Outside A Waterfront Saloon

Chappell

Ellie reappears. She passes by

Ravenal and drops her handkerchief; Ravenal restores it politely to her hand.

Dialogue ELLIE and RAVENAL
A la valse

Exit Ravenal

lunga
pausa

Chappell

No. 7

Life On The Wicked Stage

(Ellie and Girls)

hold your hand, (which means an ex-tra beer or sand-wich)

Ev-'ry-bod-y whis-pers: "Ain't her life a whirl?"

Though you're warned a-gainst a rou-é ru-in-ing your re-pu-

-ta-tion, When you've played a-round the one night trade A-round a

Chappell

great big na - tion, Wild old men who give you

jewels and sab - les On - ly live in Ae - sop's Fa - bles.

Girls

a tempo.
mf
Though we've lis-ten'd to you

Ellie

rall.
Life up-on the wick-ed stage is no-thing for a girl! ———

a tempo.

Chappell

GIRLS

moan and grieve, You must par-don us if we do not be-lieve you,

There is no doubt you're cra-zy a-bout your aw - ful stage.

ELLIE

I ad-mit it's fun to smear my face with paint Caus-ing ev-'ry one to

think I'm what I ain't, And I like to play a de-mi mond-y

role with soul! Ask the he-ro does he like the way I lure

When I play a hus-sy or a par-a-mour, Yet when once the cur-tain's

poco rit

down my life is pure And how I dread it!

colla voce

a tempo. *mf* GIRLS

mf a tempo.

Life up-on the wick-ed stage ain't ev-er what a girl sup -

Chappell

-pos - es, Stage door John-nies are-n't rag-ing ov - er you with

gems and ros - es. **ELLIE** If some gen - tle-man would talk with rea-son

poco rall. I would can-cel all next sea-son. Life up - on the wick-ed

a tempo. **GIRLS** stage ain't no-thin' for a girl. You'd be back the sea-son af-ter!

Chappell

Chappell

Till Good Luck Comes My Way

(Ravenal and Men)

lot — have their fate se-cure in a guard-ed spot of the world, — They're wel-come to their drab — — ca - reer. —

Poco meno

mf

Men

It is all well e - nough to be grin-ning while your win-nings

It is ea - - sy to be grin-ning while your stack is

mf

Chappell

Allargando

turn,——— It's bound to turn.——— Till

Moderato

good luck comes my way I'll play a - long,———

— While there's a game on the high - way I'll

stray a - long——— With just the

There may be sun - shine to - mor - row to fill the day.—— While I've a heart and a brain And my eb - o - ny cane I can bor - - row Un - til the day when good - luck comes my

Ravenal: plain.————— Live in vain, so I will

Men: For-tune will change like an Ap-ril day,——— So we will

mf cres — — — -cen — — -do   *f*

Ravenal: wait till good luck will come my way.—————

Men: wait till good luck comes my way.—————

rall.

Chappell

Scene IV
Auditorium And Stage Of The "Cotton Blossom"

No. 9

ANDY   *"Prompt her, Nola"*
MAGNOLIA   *"Hamilton, my own!"*   *"Papa! look at Julie!"*

Chappell

Chappell

Andantino
Frank calls Ravenal in.   Joe is discovered in upper box of auditorium.

Enter Ravenal

non legato

sempre pp

                                                                      Chappell

Valse

Fl.

Solo Violin

pp

ten.

Violin

Chappell

Piu mosso

Enter Magnolia, followed by Julie

Lento assai

Dolce

Chappell

110

Tempo di Valse

Magnolia sees Ravenal

sempre pp

(pp)

L.H.

Ped.

Moderato *(enter Steve)*

R.H.

pp

Ped.

Chappell

Chappell

Lento

pp JOE *from upper box*

Ol' man Riv - er, Dat ol' man Riv - er, He must know sump-in', But

don't say noth-in', He jes keeps rol-lin', he keeps on rol-lin' a -

lon'. He

♩ = ♩ *Ravenal reads lines from script.*

espr.

don't plant 'ta - ters, He don't plant cot - ton, An' dem dat plants 'em is

Chappell

soon for - got - ten; But ol' man Riv - er he jes keeps roll - in' a -

lon?

Ravenal spoken: "I understand. Miss Lucy will you be mine?"

He kisses Magnolia.

poco a poco cresc.

But

ol' man Riv - er he just keeps roll-in' a - lon?

cresc.

segue

Scene V

In Front Of The Box-office, On Foredeck Of The "Cotton Blossom"

Piano

Chappell

Chappell

I Might Fall Back On You

(Ellie and Frank)

Lit-tle girl you are safe with me: I can pro-tect what's mine; I am a sturd-y ma-ple tree and you're my cling-ing vine. Woods are just full of ma-ple trees, Ce-dar and oak and pine; Let me look them o-ver, please, And

then I'll let you know ———— If you have a show.

Af-ter I have looked a-round the world for a mate——

Then, per-haps, I might fall back on you. ————

When I am con-vinced that there is no bet-ter fate ——

Chappell

Then I might de-cide that you will do.———

FRANK
I am just an ave-rage lad, Though no gift to wo-man-hood,

Some girls say I'm not so bad. Oth-ers say you're not so good!

ELLIE

But if you are pat-ient, dear, and will-ing to wait—

Chappell

Theres a chance I might fall back on you!

GIRLS
One group of girls(to Frank)

Af - ter I have looked a - round the world for a mate

Then, per - haps, I might fall back on you!

When I am con-vinced that there is no bet-ter fate—

Then I might de-cide that you will do.———

Other group (to Ellie)

He is just an ave-rage lad, Though no gift to wo-man-hood,

Some girls say he's not so bad, Oth-ers say he's not so good!

Chappell

ALL GIRLS to FRANK

But if you are pat-ient, dear, and will-ing to wait —

There's a chance she might fall back on you!

Dance (*ben marcato*)

Cello & B'ss'n

Chappell

Chappell

Queenie's Bally - Hoo

(Queenie and Coloured Chorus)

Chappell

What fo' you gals dress up dic-ty? Where's yo' all goin'?

Tell dose sting-y men of yours to step up here in

line. _____

Meno mosso

p QUEENIE

C'mon, folks, we'se rar-in' to go, Is you or ain't you see-in' dis show?

Chappell

QUEENIE

Two seats for twen-ty cents ain't so dear! _____

Dance. Vivo

mf

Chappell

Moderato (Fox-trot tempo)

Chappell

Chappell

Scene VI

Auditorium And Stage Of The "Cotton Blossom" During the Third Act of "The Parson's Bride"

Incidental Music, played on the Stage during the presentation of "The Parson's Bride"

Chappell

Andante

© *For Villain's Entrance*

Repeat ad lib.

Repeat from © ad lib.

Chappell

Villain's Dance
(Frank's specialty dance)

Chappell

Scene VII
The Upper Deck Of The "Cotton Blossom"

Introduction And Duet "You Are Love."

Ravenal:"Er⋯no⋯not at all, I'm very thirsty!"

Moderato

a tempo

p (Magnolia whistles off stage) "That You, Nola?" Enter Magnolia

Moderato ♩=96

Cl.

Ob.

pp

rall.

deliberato

Lo stesso tempo

Viola

Cello

Valse moderato

Chappell

You Are Love

B Tempo di Valse (Ravenal and Magnolia)

Chorus.

Ravenal

Once a wand-'ring ne'er-do - well, Just a vag-rant rov-ing fel-low, I

went my way. Life was just a joke to

tell Like a lone-ly Punch-i - nel-lo My role was

gay. But I knew the joke was aim - less, Time went on I

Chappell

liked the game less, For you see, _____

Some-where lurked a spark di-vine, And I kept wond-'ring wheth-er mine Would

come to me. _____ Then — my

Poco agitato

for - tune turned and I found you. Here — you

Chappell

Chappell

Molto espress.

You ———— are Love, Here in my arms Where you be-long, And here you will stay, I'll not let you a - way, I want day af-ter day with you.——— You ——— are Spring ——— Bud of ro - mance un - furled;

(ad lib.)

tranquillo

Chappell

Chappell

Chappell

Scene VIII - Finale Act I
Levee Beside The "Cotton Blossom"

Girls: Oh, tell me, did you ev-er, Did you ev-er hear of such a thing?

Boys: The lead-ing man's a-

Girls: Her fath-er has neg-lect-ed none, He's

Boys: -bout to give the lead-ing girl a wed-ding ring, So now, you see, ro-

Girls: asked us all to see the fun, And since we are in-vit-ed to at-tend, we are de-

Boys: mance can start up-on the stage! Ro - mance

Chappell

Chappell

Chappell

Valse brillante

ENSEMBLE

Hap-py the day ——— When the hand of a maid has been won by swift pur-su - ing; Hap-py the way ——— He has chos-en to win her, by bold and ar - dent woo - ing. Their's a luck - y fate to be —— ro-man-tic,

Chappell

We can hard-ly wait to see —— The fran-tic looks of the bride-groom and quakes of the bride whom he takes now or nev-er, and makes her for - ev - er the one and the on - ly one; Who will take care that his life's not a lone-ly one while she's the on - ly one.

Chappell

Magnolia

Coloured Women

Miss Mag - nol - ia, we al - ways tol' ya, we knowed you'd

mf cresc.

Magnolia

mf

Can't I share some of my hap-pi -ness, dear friends,with

Coloured Women

find your man who'd be lov- in' you true! ———

sffz

Chappell

Chappell

Ensemble

May-be I know.— Can't help lov-in' that man of mine.————

Lively

BUCK & WING
Clar's. & Bassoon

mf

p cresc.

Enter Dancing Girls

f

Dance
Banjo

mf

Chappell

156

29678

Chappell

Chappell

Entr' Acte

No. 18

Chappell

Prelude and Opening Act II
The Midway Plaisance At The Chicago World's Fair

No. 19

Chappell

Chappell

Chappell

Chappell

166

Chappell

3rd Barker: Step clos-er, gent-le-men; You no-tice "la-dies" I don't men-tion!

Moderato

(Sings)

3rd Barker: My sto-ry's

Chorus (GIRLS): Good-ness, gra-cious me! What ev-er can it be?

p a tempo.

3rd Barker: quick-ly told:— The world's sen-sa-tion now be-

Chappell

Chappell

noth-ing wrong,— She's a prin-cess:——— From bet-ter folks than us I

Girls.

You can stay, but I must run.

Boys.

guess All right! You al-ways spoil my fun.

Vivace (♩=♩)

Chorus

Belles and beaux, Dressed in the ve-ry la-test

Chappell

Chappell

Chorus.

You can tell ev - 'ry swell

Chorus.

By his dash - ing air.

Chorus.

They do cred - it to Chi - ca - go.

Chorus

With their clothes all tai-lor made.

With their clothes the lat-est on the "Mid - way"

Chorus

All their Coun-try Cou-sins gape and stare When they

Chorus

see the dan-dies on Pa - rade.

sffz

D.S. for exit
(senza voce)

Chappell

Incidental
(Fatima's 2nd Dance)

Why Do I Love You?

No. 20   Magnolia, Ravenal, Cap. Andy, Parthy and Ensemble

MAGNOLIA

I'm walk - ing on the air, dear, —— For life is fair, dear, ——

to lov - ers; I'm in ── the sev-enth

heav - en ── (There's more than sev - en, ── my heart dis - cov -

RAVENAL

- ers,) In this sweet, im - pro - ba - ble and un - real

world, Find-ing you has giv-en me my i - deal world.

Chappell

Chappell

MAGNOLIA

You're a luck-y boy, I am luck-y too,

TOGETHER

All our dreams of joy Seem to come true; —

May-be that's — be-cause you love me,

May-be that's why I love you! —

Chappell

Chappell

Chappell

Chappell

Chappell

joy seem to come true. — May-be that's — be-cause you love me, May-be that's why I love you! —

Valse

Dance

mf dolce, con espressione

Chappell

A la Fox-Trot

CHORUS

You're a luck-y boy! I am luck-y too! All our dreams of joy Seem to come true.—— May-be that's —— be-cause you

Chappell

entrance Cap. Andy & Parthy

love me, May-be that's why I love you!

CAPTAIN ANDY

Why do I love you? Why do you love me? Why should there be

two hap-py as we? — Can you see — the why or

where - fore, I should be — the one you care for?

Chappell

You're a luck-y boy, I am luck-y too, All our dreams of

joy seem to come true.— May-be that's — be-cause you

love me, May-be that's why I love you! —

Dance (ANDY and PARTHY)

Chappell

You're a luck-y boy! I am luck-y too! All our dreams of joy Seem to come true. May-be that's be-cause I love you! May-be that's why I love you! —

DAHOMEY
(Coloured Chorus)

Chappell

Chappell

Chappell

Chappell

Chappell

Coloured Chorus

We're glad to see those white folks go! —

Coloured Chorus

Dy-un-ga Doe! Dy-un-ga Doe!

Coloured Chorus

Dy-un-ga, Hun-gy ung gun-ga, Hun-gy ung gun-ga go!

Chappell

old New York Where your knife an' fork Gent-ly

old New York Where your knife an' fork Gent-ly

sink.　　　　　　　　　　　　We are

sink in-to juic-y lit-tle chops what's made of pork! We are

Chappell

Dance (Tempo I)

Chappell

Allegro moderato

Chappell

Scene II
A Room On Ontario Street In Chicago

Piano

Moderato

pp

(This music is played while Ellie reads Ravenal's letter)

D.S.
for Curtain

Chappell

Scene III
Rehearsal Room Of The Trocadero Music Hall

No. 23

BILL
(Julie)

Words by
P. G. WODEHOUSE and
OSCAR HAMMERSTEIN IInd

Chappell

29678

Chappell

Chappell

Can't Help Lovin' Dat Man (Reprise)

(Magnolia)

Chappell

mine! ——————— When he goes a - way That's a rain-y day, And when he comes back that day is fine —— The sun will shine. He can come home - as late as can be, —— Home with-out him - ain't no home to me, —— Can't help lov-in' dat man of mine! ——————

Chappell

Allegro *Magnolia tries and fails to sing in this tempo.*

Chappell

Scene IV
Trocadero Music Hall

Captain Andy's Entrance

*) After The Ball
(Magnolia)

CHAS. K. HARRIS

please,———— Why are you sin - gle, why

live a - lone?———— Have you no ba - bies?

Have you no home?"———— "I had a sweet-

-heart years, years a - go;———— Where she is

Chappell

now, pet, you will soon know. — List' to the

sto - ry, I'll tell it all, — I be-

-lieved her faith - less, af - ter the ball."

Moderato

Af-ter the ball is o - ver, Af-ter the break of morn, —

a tempo.

Af-ter the dan-cers leav - ing Af-ter the stars are
gone; —————— Man-y a heart is ach - ing If you could
read them all; —————— Man-y the hopes that have van - ished
Af - ter the ball.   ball.

Chimes (12 o'clock)

Scene V
In Front Of The Office Of "The Natchez Evening Democrat."

No. 26

Ol' Man River (Reprise)
(Joe)

Ol' man Riv-er, dat ol' man Riv-er, He must know sump-in' but don't say noth-in', He jes' keeps roll-in', he keeps on roll-in' a-lon'.

He don't plant ta'-ters, he don't plant cot-ton, An' dem dat plants 'em is soon for-got-ten; But ol' man Riv-er, he jes' keeps roll-in' a-lon'.

Chappell

New things come 'n ole things go But all things look De same to Joe. Folks git mad An' starts a war, An' den git glad, Don't know what for. Ah keep laughin' In-stead of cry-in', Ah mus' keep liv-in' Un-til ah'm dy-in', But ol' man Riv-er, he jes' keeps roll-in' a - lon'!

f cresc.

allarg.

Scene VI
Top Deck Of The New "Cotton Blossom"

You Are Love (Reprise)
(Ravenal)

dolcissimo

RAVENAL   *"Is that you, Nola?"*

RAVENAL
mp
You   taught me to   see   one truth for - ev -   er
mp

true, —————   You —————   are   Love, —————
f

          Chappell

Won-der of all the world,————— Where you go with me Heav-en will al - ways be.

Chappell

Scene VII
Levee At Natchez

Chappell

No. 28

Dance away the night

(Kim and Chorus)

Chappell

REFRAIN.

Dance _____ away the night _____ and we can all be hap-py till the

morn - ing! Dance _____ away the night _____ and we can

stick to - geth-er till the dawn! Blue _____ will turn to

gray, _____ and when the moon steals off without a warn - ing,

Chappell

You ____ can turn and say ____ you're ve - ry glad you met us, And

then for - get us. But dance ____ away the night ____ and we can

all be hap - py till the morn - ing! Dance ____ away the

night ____ and we can stick to - geth - er till the dawn! dawn! ___

PATTER

MEN.

If you want to dance_____ here's one who's clev - - er;

Have a cav - a - lier_____ with style and tone._____

If you're on your toes___ and kind o' fol-low-where-he-goes___ You'll find a

rhythm that you feel you could do with him for e - - ver.

Get the band to break ____ in-to a fox-___trot

Mean enough to make ____ the trees and rocks trot:

Then you won't stay still— you'll dance a-gainst your will, and

keep right on un-til the break of day! You pray to stay to

poco rall.

Chappell

REFRAIN.

OMNES

Dance _____ away the night _____ and we can all be hap-py till the

morn - ing! Dance _____ away the night _____ and we can

stick to - geth - er till the dawn! Blue _____ will turn to

gray, _____ and when the moon steals off without a warn - ing,

Chappell

You _____ can turn and say _____ you're ve - ry glad you met us, And

OMNES

then for - get us. But dance _____ away the night _____ and we can

all be hap - py till the morn - ing! Dance _____ away the

night _____ and we can stick to - geth - er till the dawn! _____

Finale

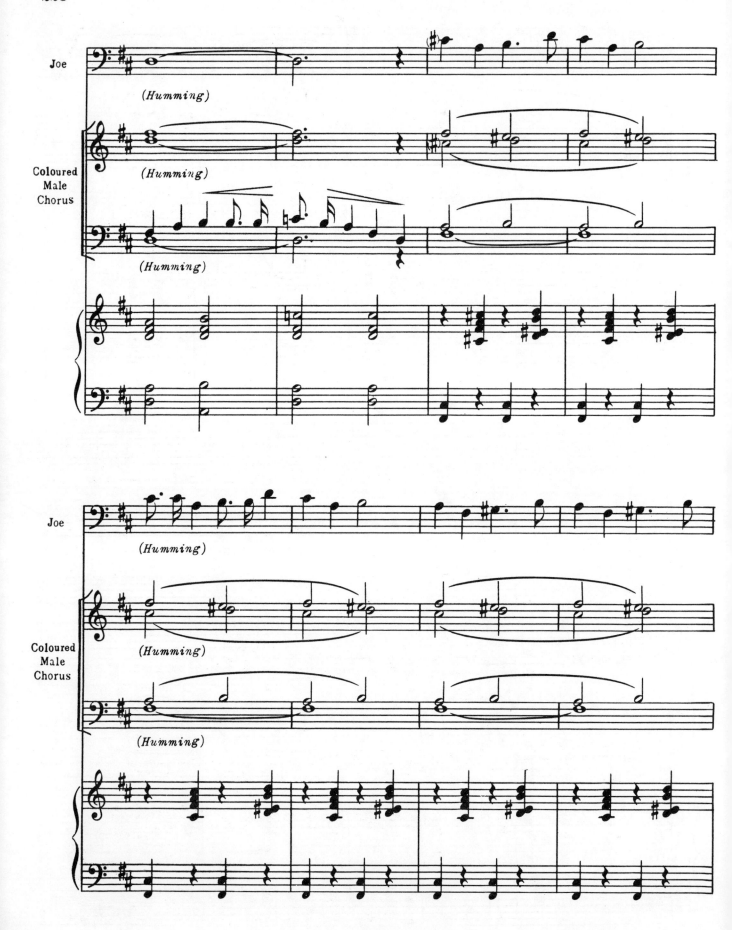

Chappell

Printed in Great Britain by Hobbs the Printers of Southampton 10/85

END OF OPERA